Coping with memory problems

Jo

A...

Gardens
WORTHING

843561
or 843530.

Coping with memory problems

Published by
Thames Valley Test Company
7–9 The Green
Flempton
Bury St Edmunds
Suffolk IP28 6EL
England

Designed by
Andrew Boag
Typographic problem solving

Photography
Matt Wilson

Printed by
Herald Graphics
Reading, England

ISBN 1 874261 11 3

Coping with memory problems

A practical guide for people with memory impairments, their relatives, friends, and carers

Linda Clare and Barbara A. Wilson

BURY ST EDMUNDS: Thames Valley Test Company

1997

Contents

Introduction

This book has been written for people with memory problems, their relatives, friends and carers.

We developed the idea for the book as we began to draft an information leaflet for people referred to the Memory Clinic at Addenbrooke's Hospital. Some of these people, diagnosed as having memory impairments, wanted to know more about how they could help themselves. Relatives, friends and carers, too, were glad of information about what they could do to make everyday life a little easier.

In preparing the book, we have been thinking of the needs of people with memory loss resulting from an illness, such as Alzheimer's disease, or an injury to the brain, for example a head injury. We have tried to explain some important facts about memory problems and to describe ways of tackling practical, day-to-day needs. We have included at the end of the book a list of 'Useful addresses'.

All of us experience memory lapses from time to time, especially if we are under pressure. We have not focused specifically on what to do about mild memory problems of this kind. However, many of the ideas we describe can be equally useful for people who just want to function more efficiently and avoid embarrassing or irritating lapses.

We are very grateful to all the people who have taken the time to participate in our research and further our understanding of how to help patients and relatives cope with memory problems. Special thanks are due to Professor John Hodges for supporting this project and to the following people for their helpful comments: Kristin Breen, Gillian Cohen, Chris Crouch, Hazel Emslie, Janet and John Hallam, Iris and Ted Hunt, Victor and Jean Jackson, Sue Kime, Pauline and Peter Lee, Nadina Lincoln, Brenda Maister, Linda Manning,

Agnes Shiel, Gordon and Sheila Tuffnail, Ray and Joan Wesson, and Headway House Cambridge. This work was supported in part by Anglia and Oxford Regional Health Authority (Research and Development). We would like to acknowledge Lifespan Healthcare NHS Trust for their support in the production of this book. We would also like to thank friends, patients, relatives, and staff who agreed to act as models for the photographs in this book. While the examples they illustrate are certainly real, we wish to emphasise that the people in the photographs do not themselves suffer from the impairments described.

Linda Clare · Barbara A. Wilson

Chapter 1: **What is memory?**

We often talk about someone having a 'good memory' or a 'bad memory'. This makes it sound as if memory is just one skill or ability. In fact, though, memory consists of several different parts or skills, which work in different ways.

People with memory problems often ask questions like these:

- Why is it that I can remember things that happened a long time ago, but I can't take in what people say to me or remember what happened yesterday?
- How come I can recognise people's faces without any trouble at all, yet have no idea of their names, even though I've known them a long time?
- Why is it that, although I know a particular piece of information perfectly well, my mind goes blank when I need to say it?

The answer to all these questions is that memory is not one function, but several; and different parts of memory can work quite separately. It helps to think about memory in terms of the various aspects which contribute to it, especially when trying to understand more about memory problems and what to do about them. In this chapter we will describe these different aspects of memory and show how we can use this framework to understand more about memory problems.

For readers who are more concerned with picking up practical tips on dealing with memory problems, this background information is not essential, but we do recommend that you try to read this chapter if possible. This is because having a better understanding of how memory usually works can help you to be more effective in tackling the kinds of problems that arise when memory goes wrong.

Key points

- Memory consists of several different aspects or functions.

- In people with memory impairments, some of these functions may be affected while others are not.

What are the different aspects of memory?

When we think about memory, it is useful to divide it into several categories or functions. Memory can be divided up in terms of:

- the time period involved, or how long-standing the memory is
- the type of information to be remembered
- what form the information is in
- stages of the memory process, or remembering
- the kind of remembering that is needed
- whether the memory dates from before or after an injury or illness.

We will say a little more about each of these aspects and how someone with a memory problem might be affected. As you read, you may like to think about how they apply to you, or to your memory-impaired relative or friend.

What time period is involved?

One very important aspect of memory is the length of time which has elapsed between taking information in and needing to remember it. Using this approach, we can divide memory into:

- immediate or working memory
- long-term memory
- prospective memory.

These three memory functions all cover different time periods, and work quite separately:

Immediate or working memory
This is memory for information from the previous few seconds. For example, we are using this aspect of memory when we look up a telephone number and hold it in our mind for just long enough to dial it.

Long-term memory
This is a separate system in which information is stored until it is needed again. Long-term memory is made up

of several parts, including delayed memory, recent memory, and remote memory.

- *delayed memory* is memory for events that happened or information that was presented in the previous few minutes. We would be using delayed memory if we had tried hard to commit the phone number in our previous example to memory and were lucky enough to be able to remember it half an hour after we dialled it.
- *recent memory* is memory for events that happened or information that was presented in the previous few days or weeks, for example what we did last weekend.
- *remote memory* is memory for events that happened or information that has been collected over several years, for example things that happened when we were at school.

Prospective memory

This is memory for things we are planning to do in the future, for example remembering to telephone a friend, attend a hospital appointment next month or send a birthday card at the right time.

HOW ARE PEOPLE WITH
A MEMORY PROBLEM AFFECTED?

Usually, when someone has a memory problem, some of these functions are affected much more than others, and some may not be affected at all. For example, people whose memory has been damaged in some way are usually able to remember a telephone number for long enough to dial it, showing that their immediate memory is not affected. They often find it relatively easy to remember things that happened to them a long time ago, which tells us that their remote memory is fairly intact. However, they usually find it very difficult to take in new information and remember it after a short delay or distraction; for example, they may quickly forget an important telephone message. Prospective memory is also often affected, with people finding it hard to remember appointments and other things they need to do.

What type of information needs to be remembered?
The kind of information or material to be remembered might involve:
* facts
* personal experiences
* skills, routines and procedures for doing things.

Memory copes quite differently with these different kinds of information.

Memory for facts
Facts are things we have learnt at some time, such as the fact that Paris is the capital of France, or that King Henry VIII of England had six wives, or the fact that both dogs and cats are furry animals with four legs, but cats miaow while dogs bark. Usually, we don't remember exactly where we gained this kind of knowledge; we only know that we have gradually accumulated it over the years.

Memory for personal experiences
Things that happen to us form more personal memories, ranging from what we just had for lunch to early childhood events such as our first day at school.

Memory for skills and procedures
This means remembering how to do something such as driving a car, sewing on a button, or using a computer to write and print a letter. Skills of this kind become quite automatic with practice.

HOW ARE PEOPLE WITH A MEMORY PROBLEM AFFECTED?
Sometimes people with a memory impairment have much more difficulty with memory for personal experiences than memory for facts. They may have trouble remembering things that have happened to them, but

still retain much of their factual knowledge. A few people have the opposite pattern, losing some of their factual knowledge while still being able to remember things that happen to them.

Even if people have considerable difficulties with memory for facts or personal experiences, their memory for skills often remains as good as before. Some people can have quite a lot of difficulty remembering new facts or recent events, such as the name of the current President or Prime Minister, or who came to visit the previous day, but still remember how to perform skills such as driving a car, doing the washing, or playing the piano. They may even be able to learn new skills despite their memory problems.

What form does the information take?
The kind of things we take in and store in memory can come in various forms. The most important distinction here is between *verbal* and *visual* memory.

- *Verbal memory* is memory for information in the form of words, whether written or spoken.
- *Visual memory* is memory for things that have to be remembered in visual form, such as faces, patterns or the layout of a building.

HOW ARE PEOPLE WITH
A MEMORY PROBLEM AFFECTED?
Some people with memory problems find it much easier to remember something they have seen than something they have heard or read. For example, they may have a very good memory for faces, but have tremendous difficulty remembering names. Others may show the opposite pattern, for example they may be able to memorize lines of poetry but still be completely unable to find their way around a building they visit often. If this is the case, it is very helpful to know about it when trying to plan ways of helping with the problems.

What are the stages of the memory process?

Remembering itself is not one skill but a process made up of several different skills or abilities. The ability to remember something involves three separate stages, called *encoding, storage,* and *retrieval.* Some people find it helpful to think of this as being rather like finding a book in a library.

- *Encoding* involves taking the information in and registering it. In our example, a new book is given a code by the librarian and entered in the catalogue in the correct place.
- *Storage* involves putting the information into memory until it is needed again, and keeping it in a place which makes it easy to find. In our library example, the book is put on the shelves in the correct section, which is often arranged in alphabetical order.
- *Retrieval* involves recalling the memory when it is needed. In our example, a library user who wants the book must be able to look it up in the catalogue, find out where it is located, and collect it from the shelf.

Our ability to remember can be affected by difficulties with any one of these stages. Continuing our analogy of the library book, if the librarian does not enter the book in the catalogue and make it part of the library, no one will be able to get hold of it. If the book is stored in the wrong section, no one will be able to find it, even though it is somewhere in the library. Finally, if the library user does not know how to use the code listed in the catalogue to find the book, he or she will be unable to locate and read it. Applying this to memory, we can see that if the information is never registered in the first place, it will not be there later on when it is needed. If it is registered but is stored wrongly, it will be impossible to find. Similarly, if the ability to look for it in the right way is lacking, then although the information is there it will not be found when it is needed.

HOW ARE PEOPLE
WITH MEMORY PROBLEMS AFFECTED?

People with memory problems may find that any one, or more, of the three stages is affected. They may have difficulty either *taking things in*, or *storing them* in memory, or *finding them again* when they are needed. We all know the feeling of having someone's name 'on the tip of the tongue' – we know that we have learned the name in the past, and that we have stored the information in memory, but we simply cannot remember it at the right moment. This is a very common experience for people with a memory problem, and leads to a great deal of frustration.

What kind of remembering is needed?

Sometimes we need to get hold of information stored in memory without any outside help. We have to actively *recall* the information. If we are lucky, there may be some clues to help us. For example, if we try to remember what we heard on the news earlier in the evening in order to inform a friend who has just come in, it might help if our friend asks a question which happens to jog our memory.

Sometimes we just need to *recognise* that we have seen something or someone before. If we are trying to find our way to somewhere we have been once before, we will probably be able to recognise some familiar landmarks which help guide us to our destination.

Recognising something you have seen, read, or heard before can often be easier than recalling it. You may be able to recognise a favourite piece of music easily from hearing the first few notes, even though you cannot sing the first few notes when someone asks you what the piece of music sounds like. Similarly, it can be much easier to find your way to somewhere you have been once or twice before than to describe the route to someone else.

HOW ARE PEOPLE WITH
A MEMORY PROBLEM AFFECTED?

People with a memory problem often find it easier to recognise familiar things than to recall information from memory. For example, they may find it quite easy to recognise friends and colleagues but have a great deal of difficulty recalling the names of these individuals.

Does the memory date from before or after the injury or illness?

When someone has had an injury or illness, we can draw a distinction between memories which were laid down before the injury or illness, and memories for events and information from the period since the injury or illness. The term *retrograde* memory is used to refer to the former category, while the latter category is referred to as *anterograde* memory.

- *Retrograde memory* is memory for events and information from before the injury or illness which has resulted in memory problems. This term refers to old learning, or learning which took place before the injury.
- *Anterograde memory* is memory for events and information from the period following the injury or illness which has led to memory problems. This term refers to new learning, or learning which has taken place since the injury.

HOW ARE PEOPLE WITH
A MEMORY PROBLEM AFFECTED?

This depends very much on what has caused the problems. Quite often, someone with a memory problem will have difficulties with anterograde memory, or new learning, while their memory for times before the injury or illness will be reasonably intact. Sometimes, however, retrograde memory, or old learning, is also affected. In some cases, the extent to which old learning is affected varies; older memories remain relatively intact but there is a gradual decline over time so that memories from the period immediately before the illness are most affected. Sometimes, after a brain injury, the person may have a complete loss of memory for a period of time before the injury. The period of time involved can range from a few minutes to a number of years.

Conclusion: a variety of functions

In this chapter we have described memory as consisting of a number of different functions. Using this framework makes it clear that memory problems can be quite varied in nature, affecting different aspects of memory functioning. In the next chapter we will go on to talk more about what it is like to have a memory problem and how memory problems are assessed.

- Memory problems can be very general, affecting most aspects of memory, or they can be more specific, affecting only one aspect such as remembering names.

- People with memory impairments experience a range of day-to-day problems that make it hard to cope and also cause stress for relatives.

- Having a memory problem does not mean you are 'stupid' or 'going crazy'.

- Memory performance is likely to be worse for anyone who is stressed, depressed, anxious, tired, or unwell.

- Assessment of memory problems usually involves seeing a medical specialist and a pyschologist, and perhaps having a brain scan.

Chapter 2: **What does it mean to have a memory problem?**

What causes memory problems?

We all experience lapses of memory occasionally, and this can happen more often as we get older. Sometimes if we are under stress or trying to do several things at once it is hard to concentrate, and then we start to forget or become muddled. Our memory can seem worse if we are unwell or just tired at the end of a long day. This kind of variation is perfectly normal.

Severe memory problems are much more obvious and persistent. Severe memory problems can result from various causes, for example:
- a dementia-type illness, such as Alzheimer's disease
- a head injury or other injury to the brain
- conditions such as epilepsy
- some kinds of stroke
- shortage of oxygen to the brain, for example because of a heart attack
- infections of the brain, for example encephalitis, which is caused by a virus.

What are memory problems like?

Because there are various different causes of memory problems, and because memory itself consists of various different skills, memory problems can take a variety of different patterns. The problems may be very general, affecting several aspects of memory, or very specific, affecting just one aspect. Often, the problems are fairly general, affecting a number of aspects of memory.

Although everyone is different, some characteristic features are shared by a large proportion of people with memory problems. We know that the majority of memory-impaired people:
- have normal or near-normal immediate memory – for example, they can remember a telephone number for long enough to dial it

- have difficulty remembering things after a delay or distraction – for example, they may completely forget something they were told half an hour ago
- have problems in learning new information – for example, when they meet someone new they may have trouble remembering the person's name
- remember things that happened some time before their injury or illness better than things which happened a short time before it – for example, they may remember childhood experiences very clearly whereas they cannot recall much about events in the year before their injury
- remember how to do things they were good at or had practised a great deal – such as playing the piano, swimming or driving a car
- are helped to remember by cues – for example, giving the first letter of someone's name may help them to remember the name.

Depending on the cause, memory problems may stay the same over time, or they may improve or get worse. Although some people who have had brain injuries can expect to see at least some improvement in their memory over time, others find the problems stay just the same, while people with illnesses like dementia find that their problems tend to increase slowly as time goes on.

Very severe memory difficulties are sometimes referred to as *amnesia*. A person might be termed *amnesic* if he or she has major problems with memory, especially with taking in and storing new information, but other aspects of mental functioning, such as reasoning, language, and perception, are reasonably intact.

Are there other problems that can be mistaken for memory difficulties?

Sometimes memory problems can be the end result of a different kind of underlying problem. We mentioned in Chapter 1 that if information is not taken in properly it cannot be stored in memory and later retrieved, so the person's memory performance will be poor. Difficulties with attention and concentration can interfere with the ability to take information in, and so disrupt memory performance. A thorough assessment can help to identify precisely what the problems are, and this in turn helps in deciding how to tackle the difficulties and find ways of coping.

Some difficulties, which result from quite different causes, can seem very much like memory problems to relatives and friends. For example, a person may seem to those around him to be 'forgetting' words, when in fact this is the result of a language disorder and would be seen as a word-finding problem or a form of *dysphasia*. Someone with a problem of this kind may have a perfectly good memory. Similarly, someone who can no longer dress herself may seem to have 'forgotten' how to put her clothes on, whereas professionals would see this as a difficulty in planning, co-ordinating, and sequencing actions and movements, or *dyspraxia*. Again, someone with a problem of this kind may have a perfectly good memory. Although of course these problems do frequently occur together with memory impairments, they are separate and need to be tackled in a different way to memory problems.

What kinds of everyday difficulties do memory-impaired people experience?

Severe memory problems have a huge impact on everyday life. People with serious memory impairment experience a number of day-to-day problems. Some of the most common difficulties for memory-impaired people include:

- forgetting what they have been told
- forgetting people's names
- forgetting where they have put things
- getting lost in both familiar and unfamiliar places
- forgetting a change in routine
- forgetting to do something important

- forgetting whether or not they have done something
- forgetting appointments
- asking the same question over and over again
- repeating the same story again and again.

These kinds of problems can make it very hard for the memory-impaired person to cope with daily life and to remain independent. They can also cause a lot of stress for partners, relatives, carers, and friends.

Is the person with a memory problem 'stupid' or 'going crazy'?

People who have a memory impairment sometimes say they feel as if they must be 'stupid', or fear they are 'going crazy'. Having a memory problem most definitely does not mean that either of these things are true.

Memory problems occur when part of the brain is damaged or is not working properly. Fundamentally this is no different from any other kind of illness or injury. People with memory impairments usually have other skills and abilities which are just as good as before. The important thing is to make use of these other skills and abilities to help compensate for the memory problems. Even people whose memory problems are very severe, and who have other additional problems as well, can be helped to develop coping strategies and find ways of compensating. We will say more about this in the next chapter.

Does stress make memory problems worse?

How we feel in ourselves can have a marked effect on memory. Memory performance is likely to be worse in someone who is feeling depressed, anxious, stressed, unwell, or overtired. Sometimes it can even seem as if the person has a severe memory problem, when in fact the poor performance is due to these other factors. For most people, the apparent memory problems resolve once mood has improved and well-being is restored.

People who already have severe memory problems are likely to have periods of feeling anxious or depressed because of the way in which their memory difficulties affect their day-to-day life. This in turn can make the memory problems seem even worse. If you do have memory problems, it is important to try not to be too hard on yourself. If you are a relative or friend of a memory-impaired person, it is helpful to try to make sure the person does not experience too much stress, and that he or she has as much support as possible.

Memory problems can be stressful for everyone in the family, and may sometimes lead to friction or arguments. Other family members may benefit from having some help and support, for example from a voluntary or self-help group.

Does memory get worse as we get older?

Older people benefit from a greater wealth of experience than younger adults, so they have some important advantages. However, they are more likely to suffer from loss of hearing or vision and from physical health problems, all of which can affect memory performance.

There do seem to be changes in the way we think and process information as we get older. We process information more slowly and become less flexible in allocating mental resources between different tasks and priorities. Changes in memory itself, however, are relatively minor (Woods & Britton, 1985). Working memory is not really affected, so that, for example, the ability to retain a telephone number in memory long enough to dial it is usually intact. Remote memory is also usually unaffected, and many older people can describe events from their early lives in great detail. The aspects of memory which can be mildly affected are delayed and recent memory – the ability to take information in and recall it after a few minutes, hours, days, or weeks. This is the source of the memory lapses which older people describe as happening more frequently than when they were younger.

It is difficult to make general statements about older people, because – as with any age group – there are a lot of differences between individuals. On the whole, though, older people do not automatically develop memory problems, and most have only mild or occasional difficulties. These are quite distinct from the kinds of severe memory problems experienced by the minority of older people who develop a dementia-type illness.

How are memory problems assessed?

Assessment of memory problems usually involves seeing a medical specialist and a psychologist, and perhaps having a brain scan.

What does the medical specialist do?

People who are referred to a specialist for an assessment of their memory usually start by seeing a medical doctor specializing in either neurology, psychiatry or the care of older people. It is very important to check that there are no medical problems, as memory difficulties can some-times be the result of other illnesses or medical condi-tions, which can be put right by appropriate treatment. Of course, people who have a brain injury, such as a head injury or stroke, will also first of all receive the nec-essary medical care, often as an in-patient. The medical investigations may include a brain scan.

What does having a brain scan involve?

The doctor may suggest that you have a brain scan. A scan gives a picture of the brain structures or of the blood circulation in the brain. This enables the doctor to see if there are any problems in the way the brain is working and, if so, where these are occurring. There are several different kinds of scan, which give slightly differ-ent kinds of pictures. The ones most commonly used are CT, MRI, and SPECT scans. Going for a scan can seem a little daunting, but the procedures are painless and have no ill-effects. What to expect depends on the kind of scan you are having:

Having a CT scan

You will be asked to lie down and place your head on a cushioned head-rest inside the scanner, which looks like a large metal ring. You will need to lie still for a time while the scanner moves over your head. The scan gives a series of pictures showing the structures of your brain in cross-section from different vantage-points. CT stands for *Computered Tomography*.

Having an MRI scan

You will be asked to lie still on a bed which is passed slowly through the scanner, a large metal tube that creates a strong magnetic field. People sometimes feel quite claustrophobic while they are inside the scanner, and the procedure can seem rather noisy and confusing, so it is best to be prepared for this. Sometimes it is possible for a relative to stay nearby and talk to you while you are in the scanner. The scan is similar to a CT scan, but gives much more detailed pictures and allows a wider range of techniques to be applied which can help in visualizing different brain pathologies. MRI stands for *Magnetic Resonance Imaging*. This procedure is sometimes called NMR scanning; NMR stands for *Nuclear Magnetic Resonance*.

Having a SPECT scan

You will be given an injection of a radioisotope which temporarily attaches itself to your blood cells as they circulate. After about 20 to 30 minutes your brain is scanned. The scanner is more spacious than in the case of CT or MRI, and as a result some people find this procedure more comfortable. The radioisotope fades naturally out of your system and does not cause any adverse reactions or allergies. The scan gives a picture of how blood flows through your brain. This provides information on the level of brain metabolism or activity.

A SPECT scan may therefore reveal abnormalities which are not apparent on CT or MRI. SPECT stands for *Single Positron Emission Computed Tomography*.

What does the psychologist do?

Seeing a psychologist is another important part of the assessment. The psychologist aims to find out which aspects of the person's memory are affected, and how severely, and to assess what effect this has on everyday life. First of all the psychologist will want to find out as much as possible about the individual and the problems he or she has been experiencing. Questionnaires and checklists are sometimes used to gather answers to important questions, and usually both the person being assessed and a relative or close friend will be asked to complete separate versions.

As well as asking about the memory problems, the psychologist uses a range of tests, which are structured tasks designed to assess different aspects of memory and thinking. The psychologist can compare an individual's scores on these tests with the scores that would usually be expected for someone of a similar age who does not have a brain injury or illness. It is also possible to make comparisons with the results that would be expected in people with certain kinds of brain damage. This allows the psychologist to see exactly which aspects of memory are affected and, where appropriate, to get an idea of how likely it is that the person has a particular kind of illness or damage to the brain. Sometimes the psychologist may recommend that the tests are repeated at intervals, usually at least six months to a year, in order to gauge progress or changes over time.

If you see a psychologist for assessment, the kinds of things you will be asked to do might include:

- learning some names
- saying the meanings of words
- repeating numbers, rather like telephone numbers

- remembering a short story and retelling as much of it as you can
- copying designs
- memorizing designs and drawing them from memory
- matching patterns
- recognizing pictures or words you have been shown previously
- responding to drawings of familiar objects by saying what they are
- remembering to ask the psychologist a question at a particular time.

People often feel nervous about the idea of being tested, and they may think back to unpleasant experiences of doing tests or exams when they were younger. The kinds of tests the psychologist uses are not meant to be like this. If you are being assessed, the psychologist will want to make sure you do your best. Some of the tests will certainly seem demanding. However, they are not designed to trick you or mark you down, and they are not meant to be competitive. The psychologist will be aiming to get a picture of both your strengths and your needs, and to understand how to build on your strengths in order to address your needs or areas of difficulty. The important thing is just to do the best you can.

What specialist help is available for people with memory problems?

Many major hospitals have a specialist assessment service for people experiencing memory difficulties. In some places this is called a Memory Clinic. In a Memory Clinic various different professionals, including a medical specialist and a psychologist, and perhaps also an occupational therapist or specialist nurse, work closely together to assess people with a memory problem and advise on further help.

Some people with memory and other problems may be offered a period of rehabilitation at a special centre, either as an in-patient or as an out-patient. Others may receive help and advice from a psychologist, occupational therapist, or community nurse. It is worth finding out what help is available in your local area.

Voluntary organizations and local self-help schemes may be able to offer practical help, such as assistance with shopping or finding someone who can stay with the person while the carer goes out for a while, or providing social activities, such as a discussion group or lunch club. Again, it is well worth exploring what is available locally. The list of 'Useful addresses' at the end of this book should give you some idea of where to start.

Conclusion

We began this chapter by describing what it is like to have a severe memory problem. Sometimes poor memory performance can be the result of other underlying problems, and this is one reason why a thorough assessment is important. Assessment also helps to establish exactly which aspects of memory are affected, and what sort of approaches may be helpful in dealing with the problem. There are some sources of specialist help available. More important, there is a great deal that individuals and their families or carers can do themselves in order to cope effectively with memory problems. In the next chapter we will go on to talk about ways of adapting, coping, and making life easier.

Key points

- There is no simple cure for memory problems but there are ways of coping with the problems and making life easier.

- There are many kinds of aids and adaptations which can be used.

- Using strategies and external aids to help with memory is not 'cheating' – it is important to make use of anything that will help.

- These kinds of approaches can help with the emotional and practical consequences of having a memory problem or caring for someone with a memory problem.

Chapter 3: **How can we adapt and cope?**

Unfortunately, we do not have a simple cure for memory problems. The good news, though, is that there are a number of things that can be done to help and which can make living with memory problems easier. It is usually possible to find some ways of adapting to memory problems, and in this chapter we will focus on practical strategies for adapting and coping. Sometimes it is also possible to find ways of helping people store and recall memories more effectively, and we will say more about this in the next chapter.

How can I make life easier?

There are a number of ways to make life easier. These include:

- adapting the environment
- using external memory aids
- following a set routine
- combining several strategies to make a substitute 'memory system'
- improving general well-being.

We will talk about each of these in turn.

Making life easier by adapting the environment

One very effective way of helping people with memory problems is to adapt their surroundings so that they have less need to rely on their memory.

These sorts of changes are often fairly straightforward to make. Here is a range of ideas that other people have found useful in their own particular situation:

- Keeping a notepad by the phone to make a note of phone calls and messages.
- Putting essential information on a noticeboard or memo board.
- Deciding on a special place to keep things like a handbag, pair of glasses or set of keys, and being sure

always to put them back in the same place after using them.

- Attaching important items so they can't be mislaid, for example using a neck cord for reading glasses or tying the front door key to a belt.
- Labelling cupboards in the kitchen as a reminder of where things are.
- Painting the toilet door in a distinctive colour so it is easier to find.
- Labelling doors as a reminder of which room is which.
- Putting a large 'stop' sign on the inside of the front door to prevent someone who is confused from wandering out of the house and getting lost.

Jennifer, who had memory problems after an attack of encephalitis, could no longer find things in the kitchen. Her family helped her to label all the cupboard doors and drawers with signs saying 'cutlery', 'plates and bowls', 'saucepans' and so on. This meant she could be sure of putting things away in the right place and finding them again when she needed them.

Sometimes it helps if relatives alter how they do things, or how they respond to the memory-impaired person. For example, some relatives decide to reply to repetitive questions in a different way, or to rephrase the questions they ask the memory-impaired person in order to avoid a predictable and irritating response.

John, a young head-injured man, always said 'Ready, willing and disabled' when asked if he was ready. This was amusing at first, but quickly became irritating when repeated on numerous occasions. John himself, of course, did not realize that he had already made the same joke many times before. The solution was to avoid asking him if he was ready. By saying something different, such as 'It's time to go now', or asking a different question, such as 'Have you got your coat on?' his relatives and friends made sure that he gave more suitable responses. Because there was no reason to get irritated, trips and outings started off on a better footing and everyone felt more relaxed.

Dorothy, who had Alzheimer's disease, often asked her husband 'What day is it today?' He was very patient, but did begin to find this a little irritating at times. She realized that it was irritating for him, but could not stop herself from asking. Her husband eventually coped with this by purchasing a calendar that showed one day at a time, and suggesting that she look at the calendar whenever she asked what day it was. To start with, he also reminded her to look at the calendar several times a day. Before long, Dorothy had got into the habit of looking at the calendar to find out what day it was and rarely asked her husband any more.

Making life easier by using external memory aids

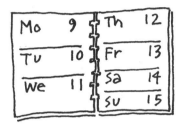

There is nothing special about the idea of using external memory aids – you will almost certainly be using them in some way or other. We all do. We keep diaries to remind us of appointments, make lists to remind us of the things we have to do, and ask others to remind us not to forget. Most of us would not manage without using some kind of external memory aid.

External memory aids are all the more important for people with memory problems. They can take over some of the tasks that memory would otherwise perform, and help to limit the number of things that have to be remembered.

ISN'T IT CHEATING TO USE A MEMORY AID?

Sometimes people with memory problems are reluctant to use external aids, saying that they do not want to become dependent on them or that they feel their memory should be able to do the work without help. While this is understandable, it is not really very realistic. As yet there is no way of curing memory problems, and it is more useful to think of the memory problem as a kind of disability for which the person needs to compensate. The idea is to use whatever aids are helpful as a way of making up for the lost memory ability and reducing the load on remaining memory so that it can operate more effectively. Most people who do not have memory problems would have difficulty in managing without some sort of memory aid, and there is nothing wrong with relying on something which helps. It is important for memory-impaired people to make use of anything that will help them. There is no evidence at all to suggest that using external aids has a damaging effect on remaining memory or that it prevents improvement where this is possible.

WHAT EXACTLY ARE EXTERNAL MEMORY AIDS?

There are a lot of things that can act as external memory aids. These include:

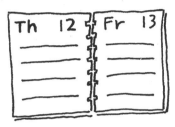

- a diary, Filofax or datebook
- notebooks
- making lists
- an alarm clock or timer
- a watch
- a calendar
- a wall chart or wipe-clean memo board
- a tape recorder or Dictaphone
- an electronic organiser
- an electronic pager
- a pill reminder box for medication
- sticky-backed notes
- a photo album or memory book.

Using an external memory aid can be as simple as putting a notebook by the phone so that any messages can be written down straight away, or making a list of 'things to do today'. There are any number of imaginative and ingenious ways of using external aids to make life easier.

Memory problems can make life quite difficult at work. Nasreen very efficiently wrote notes about important conversations and messages on pieces of paper, but invariably ended up losing them. She tackled this problem by getting an answerphone and taping all her conversations. At the end of the day she replayed the tape and made notes. She then entered any appointments in her diary and put the notes into the relevant files. Using this routine helped Nasreen to cope with her job reasonably well despite her memory problems.

After a stroke affected his memory, Michael used a wipe-clean 'memory board' that hung on the kitchen wall. On one side was listed important information such as his wife's telephone number at work and details of who to contact in an emergency. On the other, he and his wife wrote daily reminders such as the date and a list of things to do, which he ticked off when he had completed each item. This enabled Michael to cope alone while his wife was at work.

One family made a 'memory book' with their memory-impaired relative. This included photos and mementoes of important events in her past life and photos of important people in the family, including all her children and grandchildren with labels giving their names and ages. Family members used the book as a starting point for conversation with their relative (Bourgeois, 1992). A similar idea, which some families have used, is to make a video recording for their memory-impaired relative to watch.

When a daughter wanted to help her mother, who has Alzheimer's Disease, remember useful information, she made her mother a tape recording. On one side she recorded important personal details, and on the other, which was regularly updated, she included information about forthcoming events. She reminded her mother to listen to the tape and gave her mother instructions about how to operate the tape recorder during their frequent phone calls. (Arkin, 1991 & 1992).

Anna, who had memory problems due to Alzheimer's disease, still enjoyed writing to a number of penfriends around the world, but tended to forget whether or not she had replied to their letters, and often thought she had replied when in fact she had not. She was very surprised and worried when one penfriend wrote to express concern after not hearing from her for several months. This problem was tackled by buying a small notebook, which her husband adapted to be rather like an address book, with a section for each pen-friend. She was then reminded to make a note in the appropriate section every time she received or answered a letter. After a few weeks she was using the notebook without being reminded.

....

Karin, who had suffered a head injury, learnt to use a diary very effectively. As she gradually re-established her life, she began to realize that she often wore the same clothes several days in a row, because when she was getting dressed she could not remember what she had worn the previous day. She felt really embarrassed to be seen in the same clothes in this way. She solved the problem by making a daily note in her diary of what she was wearing. Each morning when she got dressed she first checked in her diary to make sure she was choosing a different outfit.

....

Aaron, who was developing Alzheimer's disease, found that although he could still drive perfectly well, he could no longer remember how to get to places. Even though he had lived in the same town all his life, and tended to visit the same places regularly, he needed help to find his way. When he needed to make a car journey he studied the map and wrote himself a list of directions on a card, which he read through several times before setting off. He took the card with him so that if necessary he could stop the car and check where he should be going next. Using this system he managed to get around the town fairly well.

....

HOW DO I CHOOSE THE RIGHT EXTERNAL MEMORY AID?

When we use external aids, we choose whatever feels right for us. Some people prefer a large diary, others a small one; some like to have a whole day to a page, others prefer to see a week at a time. The same is true for the memory-impaired person. The key thing about choosing an external memory aid is that it should suit the individual.

For example, some people find written reminders useful, such as a note taped to the telephone with the instruction to write down all messages in a notebook placed nearby. Others who find reading difficult may

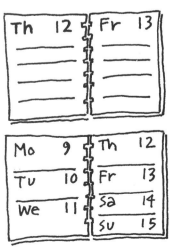

prefer pictures or diagrams, such as a pictorial label on a cupboard showing cups, saucers, and a teapot to help them find the things they need to make a drink. A few may do better with spoken instructions on a tape which they can follow at their own speed.

Similarly, people who are used to working with computers may enjoy using an electronic organizer, while people who are less comfortable with new technology will probably prefer more traditional methods such as a diary, Filofax or datebook.

Routine tasks, such as taking medication, can be listed and crossed off as they are completed; people who have difficulty writing sometimes like to use a rubber ink stamp instead.

A digital watch which shows the date, includes an alarm, and chimes regularly on the hour is a very simple, versatile, and unobtrusive aid. It alerts the person to what day it is, enabling them to find the right page in their diary. The hourly chime can act as a reminder to make a short entry in the diary about what activity one is involved in at that time. It can also serve as a prompt to check the diary in order to see if there are any tasks that need to be completed, such as doing the laundry, going to the shop, or taking medication. The chime cues the person on the hour, a particularly useful reminder for people who are not very good at judging the time.

For people who need to take medication regularly, a pill box is a valuable aid. This has sections for each day, which are subdivided into sections for each dose during the day. To help with refilling the pill box at the beginning of each week, it is a good idea to make a card giving a description of each type of medication, including its colour, size and purpose, the amount to be taken, and the timing of each dose.

It is always irritating when a familiar household appliance breaks down and has to be replaced. For Hannah, who had memory problems due to Alzheimer's disease, when her washing machine broke down it seemed as if she would never be able to do the washing again. She and her husband bought a new washing machine, but she was sure she would never be able to get used to it. Her husband decided to write down some step-by-step instructions for using the machine and to practise going through these with her while the machine was unplugged. This was quite helpful, but Hannah decided it would be better still if she wrote the instructions down in her own words. Her list of instructions was stuck on the wall above the washing machine. Using these, she was soon able to do the washing just as easily as before.

HOW EASY IS IT TO USE EXTERNAL MEMORY AIDS?

For memory-impaired people, getting used to a new memory aid can be quite demanding. At first they may forget how to use it, or leave it behind. There is no point in expecting them to adapt right away. They will probably need quite a lot of help and encouragement to enable them to make full use of the chosen memory aid. They may need reminders to take the aid with them or to use it at the right time, and they will probably need some practice in how to use it properly.

If you are thinking of introducing external memory aids, a good starting point is to build on whatever aids were used before the memory problems began. For example, people who regularly used a diary or datebook before the memory problem started usually find it relatively easy to continue, but they may need to learn to use the diary more efficiently.

Hope, who had regularly used a diary before she developed memory problems, continued to do so very effectively. However, she had difficulty remembering which day of the week it was, and so she sometimes got into a muddle about what she was meant to be doing. In order to overcome this problem, she learned to cross off each day in her diary before going to bed, so that she could check the day and date in the morning and be sure she was looking at the appointments for the right day. Just to be absolutely certain, she sometimes double-checked the date with her daily newspaper.

Memory-impaired people can sometimes get used to completely new memory aids, but they are likely to need some training and lots of opportunities to practise. The memory-impaired person may also need to be reminded to make use of the chosen external aid.

Since developing memory problems, Kirsten had difficulty organizing her time. She learnt to write a list of 'Things to do' each morning and to work her way through the various tasks. However, she still needed to be reminded to look at her list every so often.

One recent development is *NeuroPage*, a system designed in the United States, which is now being used in the United Kingdom. The idea was initially developed by an engineer as a means of helping his son, who had suffered a head injury, achieve more independence. The memory-impaired person using *NeuroPage* carries a small electronic pager, and chosen messages or reminders are fed into a computer and sent to the pager at the desired time. The person is alerted by an audible tone and then reads the message on the pager screen.

Kirsten, in the previous example, could not remember to look at her list of 'Things to do'. This was tackled using *NeuroPage*. She decided she would like to be reminded to look at her list first thing in the morning, after lunch and again at 6 p.m. The message 'Look at your list of things to do' was fed into the computer, and sent to her pager at the times she had specified. This enabled her to make sure she always checked her list three times a day.

ISN'T IT EMBARRASSING TO HAVE TO USE A MEMORY AID?

Some people do feel embarrassed at the idea of using a memory aid, and worry that they will stand out or seem odd in some way. However, as we said before, everyone uses memory aids in some form or other, often without giving it much thought, so there is no real need to feel embarrassed. To prevent embarrassment, it is best to try to use as aids things which are socially unremarkable and which might be used by anyone, such as a digital watch or diary. Far from creating a bad impression, someone using aids like these can appear well-organised and conscientious. Some memory aids, such as a pager, can actually convey status and prestige.

Making life easier by following a set routine

Another simple way of reducing memory problems is to try to follow a fairly set routine for each day or week. Having a routine means the person with a memory problem can get used to what to expect, which helps to reduce the demands on memory. Many people find it useful to make a note of regular activities in their diary or on their calendar. Another approach is to make a chart showing regular events, perhaps using pictures or photographs, and to display it on a noticeboard as a reminder.

Of course, changes in routine can be confusing, so it is usually a good idea for relatives and carers to explain any changes carefully and thoroughly. It is important to help the memory-impaired person prepare for changes well in advance, giving plenty of spoken and written reminders.

Combining several strategies to make a substitute 'memory system'

Most people with memory problems find it helps to use several aids or strategies. A relatively straightforward combination of two or three strategies can cover the areas where there would otherwise be problems, and provide a safety net for things that really must be remembered.

Injuries to the brain can have long-lasting effects. Vijay, several years after his head injury, was promoted at work and found that memory difficulties affected his ability to perform well in his new job. This made him feel more and more anxious, which in turn made it even harder for him to do his job. He began to develop several strategies for getting around these difficulties. These included:

- Three lists which he referred to regularly: one showing routine tasks to be completed each day, such as opening mail, one showing where to find his files in the filing cabinet, and one to remind him of a few key 'rules', for example that he was to do his filing each day rather than letting it mount up.
- A ring binder with sections such as 'urgent tasks' and 'long-term projects'. Vijay tended to forget that he had contacted suppliers and requested information, and therefore got into difficulty when they called him back, so there was also a section headed 'awaiting response' where he kept details of such requests.
- A notebook listing procedures for making adjustments and correcting various faults on the computer systems he looked after.
- A telephone message pad for recording each conversation as it took place, which could then be filed in the relevant file.
- Using the calendar and alarm on his computer to remind him of appointments.
- Practising assertiveness techniques to 'buy time', so that instead of feeling he must respond to colleagues' requests for help immediately, he was able to allow himself five or ten minutes to complete his current task and find the information he would need to tackle the new problem.
- Using simple relaxation and breathing exercises to reduce his anxiety.

Developing and using this system took some time and effort, but this proved well worthwhile as Vijay was able to work more effectively and felt much more self-confident as a result.

Maria, who had memory problems due to Alzheimer's disease, used a diary and pager at work before having to take early retire-ment. She continues to use a diary very efficiently for appointments, and she remembers her regular commitments such as helping at two playgroups. She also has a memory board divided into sections for each day of the week, with each day headed in a different colour – she found this in a local shop. At the start of each week she and her husband sit down with their diaries and the memory board and write down all their appointments and regular commitments, using a red pen for her engagements and a black pen for his. He also writes down what time he will be back. Quite often, when he has a meeting in town, she goes with him and visits a gallery while he is working. Afterwards they meet up. He gives her written directions of where to find him, and she arranges to receive a message on her *NeuroPage* pager telling her when it is time to set off. Usually she remembers anyway, but the message provides a safety net. Another way in which the pager comes in useful is as a reminder about medication, which she takes twice a day, ticking a chart each time. Usually she remembers, or her husband reminds her, but very occasionally they both forget, so twice a day she receives a message asking 'Have you taken your medication?' Using this combination of aids and strategies makes it possible for her to manage very well day-to-day.

People who have very severe memory problems sometimes develop quite a complex substitute memory system. This is really essential if they are to lead a normal, independent life and earn their own living. Usually they need some help to develop their system, especially in the early stages, and it takes time to adapt and refine the system so that it does everything it needs to do. Once established, though, systems like this can be very effective.

A young university student, J.C., developed severe memory loss after a brain haemorrhage. Over the following months he gradually became aware of his memory problems. He and his family worked hard to develop ways of compensating for these, with some help from the psychologist. Over the years he has continually refined his memory system. Although unable to return to university, he completed a college course and now works as a self-employed craftsman, living independently in his own apartment.

These are just some of the main components of J.C.'s memory system:

- **A Filofax (datebook)** containing a diary, details of addresses and telephone numbers, and several additional sections. He writes down all appointments in his diary and draws up a daily list of things to do. The additional sections contain colour-coded sheets with details of different aspects of his life. For example, yellow sheets contain details about friends and colleagues, such as recent meetings, ideas for future joint activities, and a note of when to telephone again. Green sheets contain details of any work needed on the apartment. Blue sheets relate to work and act as job sheets for each commission he takes on, linking with various other record-keeping systems.
- **A journal** for recording each day's main events.
- **A watch** with an alarm, into which messages and reminders can be entered. He sets the alarm to remind him to do things such as looking at his Filofax, or to ensure he leaves at the correct time if he is visiting a customer.
- **A Dictaphone**. He dictates details of events as they happen during the day, and transcribes these at night into the relevant part of his Filofax or into his journal.
- **Various lists**, for example a telephone list. He logs every telephone call he makes to ensure he does not duplicate calls, and once a call is made he enters the details into his Filofax.
- **Sticky-backed notes**. He uses these to remind himself of various tasks, such as making his packed lunch.
- **A menu chart.** This helps to make sure he gives himself a balanced and varied diet.
- **Keeping things in the same place**. Everything is kept in its own particular place and he is very careful to put things back in the right place after using them, so that he will easily find them again.
- **Following routines.** He keeps to the same routine wherever possible so as to avoid missing out important tasks, for example when getting up or going to bed.

Describing his system, he says: 'I try to make the system foolproof. It's like a web, it's hard for anything to slip through the

system. If I miss it with one thing, I'll pick it up with another –
I've individualised the system, it's constantly developing and I'm
constantly refining and correcting it.' (Wilson, J.C., & Hughes,
1997)

Making life easier by improving well-being

Memory is a very important part of our sense of who
we are. Our personal store of experience and knowledge
helps define our identity and determine how we react.
Our memory contains knowledge about other people,
which is essential to help us function in social situations,
and we draw on our memory to gauge how competent
and confident we feel in different settings. It is no
surprise that memory problems often have major
emotional consequences, including feelings of loss
and anger, and increased levels of anxiety.

HOW CAN WE IMPROVE
EMOTIONAL WELL-BEING?

People with memory difficulties often value opportunities to talk about the strong feelings that can arise as a
result of memory problems. Finding that others understand and acknowledge these feelings can provide some
relief and reassurance, and may make it easier to accept
the usefulness of trying out various practical coping
strategies.

People who have memory problems can feel very
vulnerable and unsure of themselves, and given the
practical difficulties which they face it is understandable
that they may experience a great deal of anxiety. Again,
these feelings need to be understood and acknowledged.
Anxiety can be reduced by using some of the day-to-day
strategies we have described in this chapter. In addition,
it can be helpful to try using some more general methods of managing anxiety. A simple way to start is to
identify things which the person finds soothing and
relaxing and making sure these are regularly available.
For example, these might include listening to favourite
pieces of music, having a warm bath with scented oils,

digging the garden, going for a walk or joining in a game of cards. Similarly, it helps to identify things which are particularly upsetting and to try to avoid these wherever possible. Special aids to relaxation can be purchased, such as relaxation tapes containing instructions on how to relax as well as soothing music.

Grace, who had Alzheimer's disease, felt quite vulnerable in her house and became especially anxious when it got dark. She and her husband watched the news on TV at nine o'clock every night, and she worried so much about all the nasty events which were described that, despite her considerable memory problems, she found it hard to forget about them when she went to bed. One immediate change that helped was the decision to watch the news earlier in the day. She and her husband also developed a more soothing evening routine to help her feel less scared and panicky, including listening to music, having a bath with relaxing aromatherapy oils, and enjoying a milky drink.

HOW CAN WE IMPROVE GENERAL WELL-BEING?
A sense of loss is not just the result of emotional changes; there are also many practical losses which follow as a consequence of memory problems. These can include:

- loss of structure, regular valued activities, and perhaps employment
- loss of income
- loss of enjoyment from leisure activities.

Loss of structure, regular valued activities, and employment

Loss of a job leaves people with large amounts of unstructured time and a need to develop new activities. Where people are able to return to working or studying, they may find it harder to cope and may have to put in extra effort to find ways of adapting and compensating.

Claudia had to give up her job as a midwife because of her memory problems. With the encouragement of a friend, she became a volunteer helper running crèches for the children of women attending antenatal classes. She enjoyed working with the under-fives and found they accepted her without question, so that her memory problems did not matter. Her help was appreciated so much that she was asked to work several mornings each week.

After an illness had severely affected his memory, Chai Ki gradually restructured his week. He attended a local voluntary day centre every Tuesday. On Wednesdays he joined a small group of people with disabilities making wooden articles for sale, and on Thursdays he helped the same group run a market stall. On Friday mornings he went to the gym with a volunteer helper. On the remaining days he usually visited his family or spent time with friends. He lived in his own apartment with support from care staff on site, who were able to remind him about his routine each day.

Loss of income

Financial difficulties can arise if the person with a memory problem becomes unable to work or if a carer has to give up work in order to be with the memory-impaired person all the time. Trying to find ways of coping with the memory problems and other practical difficulties may also require additional expenditure. Welfare or social security benefits go some way towards helping with this and it is important to find out what benefits you are entitled to and make sure you claim these. Information about benefits can be obtained from local advice agencies or from the nearest benefits agency office.

Mohammed Hafiz, formerly a supervisor in a factory, had not been able to work since an illness left him with epilepsy and memory problems. He received some benefits, but found it hard to make ends meet. By chance he mentioned to a visiting health worker that he was worried about money. Inquiries revealed that he was entitled to additional benefit payments, and a successful claim resulted in a considerable increase in his monthly income.

Loss of enjoyment from leisure activities

Memory problems can make it hard to do the things one used to enjoy, or they may prevent people from being able to take part in things because getting around is a problem or because social situations are anxiety-provoking. Developing new leisure activities can be well worth the extra effort involved.

Sophie had always enjoyed reading – to her, there was nothing better than a really good book. When she developed memory problems, one of her biggest losses was the ability to enjoy a book, a story or even a magazine article. She simply forgot what she had been reading too quickly. A friend brought her a book of short poems and extracts from longer poems, and she recognized several of her old favourites. She was able to gain considerable enjoyment from reading these, and poetry proved to be a reasonable substitute for her previous reading material.

Loss of contact with people

Although many people with memory problems find that friends and family are very supportive, there are unfortunately a few individuals who have little understanding of memory problems. Occasionally, for example, family members get offended because birthdays or important events have been forgotten. Sometimes it can be a good idea to try to meet new people who do have an understanding of memory problems, perhaps by joining a local discussion group or lunch club for people with similar difficulties, or attending a local voluntary centre. Some people prefer to join in social activities with other people of a similar age and similar interests who do not have particular memory problems as a way of meeting new friends. For some people, just being able to talk to someone who understands, such as a counsellor or welfare worker, is a great relief. Information about what is available in your area can be obtained from local health and social care providers, advice agencies and reference libraries, or from some of the voluntary organizations whose addresses are listed at the end of this book.

What about the needs and well-being of carers?

Emotional and practical losses and anxieties are experienced just as much by carers as by those for whom they are caring. However willingly one accepts the role of carer for a relative with memory impairments, it is not an easy task. The physical demands of caring can be a strain on health, while stress can build up as a result of isolation, lack of time to oneself, and financial worries. Assisting a memory-impaired person requires patience and tolerance, which can be hard to maintain without support from others and the chance of an occasional break. Many carers think of their own needs as far less important than those of their memory-impaired relative, without considering that their own well-being is essential if they are to continue caring effectively for their relative.

Various schemes are available to provide practical help for carers. For example, in some areas trained volunteers will stay with the memory-impaired person at home while the carer has a short break, day out or weekend away. Some carers also find it useful to attend a support group where they can meet other carers and exchange ideas and information.

Often, carers feel that things have to be extremely difficult or even desperate before they are entitled to ask for help, but in reality a small amount of help early on can sometimes prevent things building up into a crisis. It is certainly a good idea to know where to get help should you need it, for example if you yourself are taken ill and cannot care for your relative for a short while. It is well worth finding out what resources are available in your area. The list of 'Useful addresses' at the end of this book will give you some ideas about where to start.

Conclusion: adjusting to life with memory problems

In this chapter we have emphasized the importance of adapting to memory problems and finding ways of coping. Where memory problems are not going to go away, the use of memory aids and coping strategies is the most effective way of making life easier. This is not a form of cheating or giving in; on the contrary, it is a very positive and constructive way of approaching the situation. Memory problems have a considerable impact on day-to-day life and on the well-being of affected individuals and their families, so it is very important to ensure that everyone has access to pleasurable and relaxing activities, social contact, and, where necessary, short breaks from one another's company.

Many memory impaired people and carers, while accepting that adapting is important, still want to know if there is anything that can be done to improve memory. Although we cannot cure memory problems, there are some ways of helping people to make the most of their existing memory and use it more efficiently. We will discuss these in the next chapter.

Chapter 4: How can we make the most of memory?

Although we do not have a way of restoring lost memory capability, it is often possible to help people make better use of their existing memory. In this chapter we will describe how you can help to make the most of memory and what techniques might assist people with a memory impairment in the difficult task of taking in important information and remembering it when they need to.

It is sometimes possible to make memory more efficient. There are some techniques that can help memory-impaired people to:

- get information into their memory more efficiently
- store information in memory more effectively
- recall information better.

There are also methods specially designed to help older people.

How can we help people get information into memory more efficiently?

If we want to remember something, we first have to get the information into memory so that it can be stored away ready for when it is needed again. Sometimes this can take quite a bit of effort. Many memory-impaired people find it extremely difficult to take in new information, especially if it is complex or extensive. This is especially true if they have additional problems such as difficulties in concentrating and paying attention.

When you want to give some information to a memory-impaired person, it can help to follow a few simple rules:

- Concentrate on **relevant** material that the person wants or needs to remember.
- **Simplify** information and written instructions.
- **Reduce** the amount of information that has to be remembered, and just concentrate on the essentials.

Key points

- There are some methods which can help people to take in, store and recall information more efficiently.

- Memory games do not improve memory as such, but they can give people with memory problems practice in developing and using strategies for remembering better.

- Older people with memory problems can be helped to make the most of their past memories and to be more aware of the present.

47

- Divide the information into **small chunks**.
- Give the chunks **one at a time**.
- Encourage the person to take their time and pay close **attention**.
- Ensure that the information has been understood by having the person **repeat it back** in his or her own words.
- Ask the person to **make associations** by linking the new information to something that is already familiar. For example, if someone is trying to learn the name Barbara, it might help to remember that they have a cousin who is also called Barbara, or to think of a well-known singer or film star such as Barbra Streisand or Barbara Stanwyck, or perhaps to make a link with a song like the folk song 'Barbara Allen' or the catchy 'Bar-bar-bar-bar-barbara Ann'.
- Use the **little and often** rule – it is better to work for a few minutes several times a day than for a longer period once a day.
- Encourage the person to **organize** the information that needs to be remembered. For example, when making a shopping list, the items can be grouped into categories such as vegetables, dairy produce, cleaning materials and so on, or according to the shop in which they can be found.
- Use **two or three different methods** to improve learning of one piece of information. For example, if your aim is to teach the person to remember the way to the shop you could both draw a map and describe the route in words, as well as accompanying the person along the route for the first few occasions.
- Choose a **good time to practise**. Practice will be most effective when the person is feeling alert and ready. It is not a good idea to expect the person to practise when tired, for example late in the evening.

carrots
potatoes

milk
cream
eggs

bleach
polish

Do memory-impaired people learn from their mistakes?

You have probably been brought up with the idea that we learn from our mistakes. For many of us, this is absolutely true. If we make a mistake, we are quite likely to remember next time round that it was a mistake, and so we do not make the same mistake again. However, this is often not the case for memory-impaired people. If they make a mistake when learning, they are quite likely to repeat the mistake the next time round. For example, when memory-impaired people are trying to learn a new name, and guess wrongly, they tend to repeat the wrong guess the next time they are asked to try to remember the name, even though they were told of their mistake the first time round. The wrong response tends to get in the way, so it becomes even harder for them to learn effectively. To stop this happening, it is a good idea to try to prevent memory-impaired people from making mistakes when learning new information or a new skill. Psychologists call this approach 'errorless learning'.

Memory-impaired people know all too well what it is like not to be able to do things or get things right. An advantage of the errorless learning approach is that it gives people the opportunity to experience success, which is a great motivator.

Hanif was being taught the names of staff in his rehabilitation unit. He was shown photographs and asked to say the person's name. Whenever he could not remember the name, he was invited to guess. He tended to guess wrongly, and then repeat the wrong responses when asked again. This left him feeling very frustrated and despondent. His therapist decided to try an errorless learning approach instead. He was no longer allowed to guess. Instead, for each name, he was shown the photograph and told the correct name on several occasions. The therapist then asked if he could remember the name by showing him the photograph and saying 'Do you know who this is? Her name begins with J. Only tell me if you are sure you know the answer.'

This method, which ensured that he did not make any mistakes, helped him to learn and remember the names.

What about applying new knowledge in different situations?

It can be hard for people to remember something they learned in one setting when in a different setting. They may need to be taught to use the skill or information in the second setting as well as the first.

Ian became adept at drying dishes and putting them away in the correct place while he was in a rehabilitation unit after a stroke. After his return home, he wanted to help in the kitchen but had no idea where everything belonged. His wife had to teach him where to put things. Once she had shown him a number of times, he gradually remembered and was able to dry the dishes and put them away by himself.

Mood can also make a difference. When we are feeling sad we are much more tuned in to sad memories and seem to recall these more readily, whereas when we are in a happy mood we tend to be more aware of our happy memories. If we experience something when we are in a particular mood, we are more likely to remember it when we are in the same mood once again. This means that, to increase the chances of remembering, it can sometimes be useful for memory-impaired people to work on taking in a new piece of information or to practise a new skill when in various different moods or states of mind.

What other kinds of strategies have been tried?

Examples of the kinds of strategies that have been tried include:

- mnemonics
- PQRST.

MNEMONICS

Mnemonics are verbal and visual aids to learning –
sayings, rhymes, or drawings which help us remember
things more easily. For example, the rhyme 'Thirty days
hath September' helps us to remember the number of
days in each month, and the sentence 'Richard Of York
Gives Battle In Vain' is a reminder of the colours of the
rainbow – red, orange, yellow, green, blue, indigo, and
violet. This is an example of a first letter mnemonic; if
you learned to read music you may have tried using the
mnemonic Every Good Boy Deserves Favour to remember that the notes E, G, B, D, and F are represented on
the five lines of the stave, and the word FACE to remember that the notes F, A, C, and E are represented in the
four spaces between the lines.

Less commonly used are visual mnemonics to help
remember names, although these can be very effective.
One way of using a visual mnemonic is to make an
association between a name and a face. First you turn
the person's name into a mental image, then you link
a distinctive feature of the person's appearance to the
image. For example, if you needed to remember the
name of Angela Webster, whose distinctive feature is
her long fair hair, you might remember it as a mental
picture of an angel and a star, caught in a web made out
of long strands of fair hair, so Angel-Web-Star would
help you recall Angela Webster (Moffat, 1992).

Simple visual mnemonics can sometimes help memory-impaired people to remember names. It is usually
best for a relative, friend, or therapist to devise the
mnemonic and teach it to the person who has a memory
problem. It is a good idea to try drawing a picture as a
reminder of a name that has to be remembered. For
example, the name 'Neil Kinnock' might be remembered as a picture of a kneeling king knocking.

One memory-impaired woman learned to remember the name 'Stephanie' as a picture of a step and a knee.

Mnemonics can be combined with other helpful approaches, such as ensuring errorless learning, to achieve good results in learning names.

Walter wanted to learn the names of the other members of his bowls club. This was tackled by taking photographs of the club members and teaching Walter their names during training sessions at home. The names were taught one at a time. A mnemonic was developed for each which gave a clue to the first name, and which consisted of a feature of the person's appearance that could be seen in the photograph. For example, the mnemonics included:

> **Carole** with the **curl** on her forehead;
> **Gwen** with the **gleaming** smile; and, a little less politely,
> **Reg** with the **round** tummy.

Each name was practised using errorless learning methods. Walter was first given the full name to read. Then he was given the name minus the last letter and asked to complete it, and so on until he completed the whole name by himself. After this he was tested on the name over increasingly longer intervals. Walter practised naming the photographs several times a day, and soon learnt all the names. After this, the training sessions continued at the club meetings until he was able to name each of the club members when he saw them.

PQRST

This is a way of helping yourself remember something you are reading, perhaps a newspaper article or a chapter in a book. PQRST stands for:

- Preview
- Question
- Read
- State
- Test.

It can be useful for anyone to try, and some memory-impaired people have tried using PQRST. These are the steps to follow:

- **Preview** the information by scanning it to get a general idea of the content.
- Identify some **questions** you want to be able to answer after you have read it, and write them down.
- **Read** the material.
- Repeat the main points to yourself by **stating** them in summary form.
- **Test** your knowledge by seeing if you can now answer the questions you wrote down earlier.

This approach was used to help Danny, who had had a head injury and who kept asking 'Why have I got a memory problem?' He was given a verbal description of what had happened and asked to write this down. He was then assisted in using the PQRST technique. He himself identified the questions to be asked, for example 'What has happened to me?', 'When did it happen?' and 'What are my main problems now?' Each day for three weeks he was asked these questions and if he did not know he was told the correct answer. Then the full set of information was reviewed and he applied the strategy again. By this stage he was able to answer all the questions correctly.

Does simple repetition help?

We tend to assume that repeating something over and over again is a good way to learn it, but this is not necessarily true. In everyday life there are many things we hear over and over again without memorizing them. For example, we may hear the shipping forecast on the radio daily when driving to work, but only be able to recall the names of two or three of the different shipping areas.

Simple repetition on its own is not an effective way for memory-impaired people to remember new information, so it is generally best to concentrate on other strategies, or to find ways of building on repetition to make the repeated presentation of material more effective. This can be achieved by using some of the other techniques suggested in this book.

How can we help people store information in memory more effectively?

New information is most likely to be forgotten within a relatively short time after it is learned. After this period, the rate of forgetting slows down. This is true for the memory-impaired person just the same as for anyone else, except of course that it is usually harder for the memory-impaired person to learn the information in the first place.

Once information has been taken in to memory, we can help to keep it there by persuading the memory-impaired person to practise or rehearse it every so often. This is best done by testing the person immediately after seeing or hearing the information, then testing again after a slight delay, then again after a slightly longer delay, and so on. This process is continued with the intervals being lengthened gradually. Psychologists call this 'expanding rehearsal'.

In a previous example we described how one daughter made her memory-impaired mother an audio tape of relevant personal information. To help her mother remember the information, she tested her immediately after first listening to it by asking a short set of simple questions. She tested her again a few minutes later, then again after ten minutes, and again after another twenty minutes, and so on. This was very effective in helping her mother to remember the answers to the questions (Arkin, 1991 & 1992).

When using expanding rehearsal, the first interval might be 30 seconds, the second one minute, the next two minutes, the next five minutes, and so on. For people who have a severe memory impairment, it might be necessary to start with even shorter intervals, testing them after just a second or so at first, then after five or ten seconds, and so on. This approach can be remarkably effective, and it can easily be combined with other methods, such as ensuring errorless learning and using visual mnemonics.

How can we help people retrieve information from memory more effectively?

You have probably experienced how frustrating it is when you know for sure that you know something but you simply cannot remember it however hard you try. As we said in Chapter 1, it is a bit like trying to find a book in the library without knowing how the library is organized.

Retrieving information from memory can be particularly difficult for the memory-impaired person. However, there are some techniques that can help.

It is often a good idea to provide the person with a cue or prompt which allows them to get hold of the correct memory. For example, providing the first letter of a name may help the person remember the whole name.

As we said before, it is much easier to remember something if the surroundings are the same as they were when you first took it in and stored it in your memory. For example, being in the same room with the same people as you were when you first took in a piece of information can make it a lot easier to remember it again. Similarly, it can be easier to remember things when you are in the same mood or state of mind as you were when you first took them in. In order to avoid the limitations this can place on remembering, it may be desirable to teach the memory-impaired person each item of new information in a variety of situations and settings.

Do memory games help to improve memory?

Memory games can be good fun. One well-known memory game is 'Kim's game' – you probably remember this from children's parties. A selection of items is first displayed on a tray and then removed, and the task is to name as many of the items as possible. Another game which you may have come across consists of a set of cards composed of a number of matching pairs; these are laid face down and the players take turns at turning up two cards, aiming to select two identical cards by remembering where cards are positioned.

Although these games can be enjoyable, and certainly do not do any harm, there is no evidence that they improve memory. They can, however, encourage memory impaired people to realize that it helps to use a strategy for remembering, and motivate them to use compensatory strategies in other situations as well, which in turn can have a beneficial effect. Games and exercises also allow people with memory impairments to practise or rehearse different techniques for remembering, and to find out which are most helpful.

What approaches are especially useful for older people?

As we said before, some aspects of memory do get a little less efficient as we get older, and it is quite normal to notice a few mild memory difficulties. Many of the strategies we have already described can be very useful in helping older people to cope with memory problems of this kind.

Only a relatively small proportion of older people have memory problems which are severe enough to be outside the normal range, usually as a result of an illness such as Alzheimer's disease. Older people with memory problems can sometimes appear to be relatively unaware of the present; for example, they may lose track of how old they are or what year it is. In contrast, they are often able to recall incidents from long ago. While many of the strategies we have already covered can be used by older people with severe memory problems and their carers, there are two approaches that have been designed especially for older people with severe memory problems (Woods & Britton, 1985) and that build on these contrasting features. The two approaches are:

• reality orientation
• reminiscence therapy.

What is reality orientation?

Reality orientation is an approach which aims to help older people with memory problems to stay fully aware of themselves and their surroundings. Using this approach the memory-impaired person is reminded of basic information such as the date, time of day, season, and so on. The reality orientation method can be built into every interaction with the memory-impaired person, and it is also often supplemented by formal group sessions.

The members of a small group of severely memory-impaired older people were asked what the season was. No-one was quite sure, so they were invited to look out of the window and see if they could tell. One of them quickly noticed the blossom on the trees and said it must be spring. They went on to talk about other clues such as how warm it felt and what kind of clothes they were wearing. Knowing it was spring helped them work out what month it was too. The group leader wrote down the season and the month on a memory board attached to the wall, which acted as a reminder for everyone.

What is reminiscence therapy?

Reminiscence therapy is a way of encouraging older memory-impaired people to remember incidents and experiences from their past, using reminders such as old songs, photographs and clothes. For example, a selection of items from the 1920s might be presented as a starting point for reminiscing about that era. Reminiscence therapy is usually carried out in group sessions, but can easily be used individually as a general approach to conversing with a memory-impaired person.

Remembering past events, experiences, and achievements in this way can encourage people to take more interest in conversing with others, and it may help to maintain self-confidence and self-esteem.

Roy, an elderly man who had a lot of difficulties with his memory, was shown photographs of vintage cars and vans. He picked out a photograph of an ice-cream van and became quite excited as he explained that his uncle used to have a similar van. He went on to describe various incidents from his childhood where he had accompanied his uncle on his rounds with the van. These were very happy memories and really seemed to cheer him up, as well as providing a topic for conversation.

You can find out more about reminiscence therapy and reality orientation by contacting organizations working with older people, some of which are listed under 'Useful addresses' at the end of this book. Information should also be available from local health and social care providers.

Conclusion: making the most of memory

The methods for making the most of memory described in this chapter can be very useful for people with memory problems and their carers. It is important to approach them as a way of making things easier, and if possible as an enjoyable shared activity; they should not provide a means of putting the memory-impaired person under unnecessary pressure. Ideally, these techniques should be used together with the kinds of strategies discussed in earlier chapters, such as the use of external memory aids, as part of a comprehensive approach to coping with memory difficulties.

A positive message

There is no simple solution to memory difficulties, and it is generally unrealistic to expect lost memory functioning to be regained. However, the key message of this book is a positive one. As we have emphasised throughout, there *are* things that can be done to help. It *is* possible

- to help memory impaired people develop different methods of remembering, so as to compensate for their memory problem, for example by using external aids
- to help memory impaired people learn some new information, skills and routines
- to help reduce the impact of memory problems on everyday life.

In this book we have described a number of approaches and strategies as a starting point for memory-impaired people and their relatives and carers. Strategies need to be chosen carefully to suit each individual and his or her situation, and to be adapted and combined as necessary. With a little ingenuity and persistence many everyday problems can be tackled, to the benefit of all concerned.

We hope this book has given you some helpful ideas which you can adapt to your own situation in order to make living with memory problems a little easier.

Sources

Arkin, S. (1991) Memory training in early Alzheimer's Disease: an optimistic look at the field. *The American Journal of Alzheimer's Care and Related Disorders and Research,* July/August, 17–25.

Arkin, S. (1992) Audio-assisted memory training with early Alzheimer's patients: two single-subject experiments. *Clinical Gerontologist,* 12 (2), 77–96.

Bourgeois, M.S. (1992) *Conversing with Memory Impaired Individuals using Memory Aids: a Memory Aid Workbook.* Northern Speech Services Inc., P.O. Box 1247, Gaylord, Michigan 49735, USA.

Hersh, N.A. and Treadgold, L.G. (1994) *NeuroPage: the Rehabilitation of Memory Dysfunction by Prosthetic Memory and Cueing.* Hersh and Treadgold Inc., San Jose, California, USA.

Kapur, N. (1991) *Managing your Memory: a Self-Help Memory Manual for Improving Everyday Memory Skills.* Wessex Neurological Centre, Southampton General Hospital, Southampton, England.

Moffat, N. (1992) Strategies of memory therapy. In Wilson, B.A., and Moffat, N. (Eds), *Clinical Management of Memory Problems.* 2nd Ed., London, Chapman & Hall.

Squires, E., Hunkin, N. and Parkin, A.J. (1996) Memory notebook training in a case of severe amnesia: generalising from paired associate learning to real life. *Neuropsychological Rehabilitation,* 6 (1), 55–65.

Wilson, B.A. (1992) Memory therapy in practice. In Wilson, B.A., and Moffat, N. (Eds), *Clinical Management of Memory Problems.* 2nd Ed., London, Chapman and Hall.

Wilson, B.A. (1995) Management and remediation of memory problems in brain injured adults. In Baddeley, A.D., Watts F.N., & Wilson, B.A. (Eds), *Handbook of Memory Disorders.* London, Wiley.

Wilson, B.A. (1989) *Memory Problems – After Head Injury.* Headway – National Head Injuries Association, Nottingham, England.

Wilson, B.A., J.C. & Hughes, E. (1997) Coping with amnesia: the natural history of a compensatory memory system. *Neuropsychological Rehabilitation,* 7, 43–56.

Woods, R.T. & Britton, P.G. (1985) *Clinical Psychology with the Elderly.* London, Chapman and Hall.

Appendix: useful addresses

United Kingdom

Age Concern England
Bernard Sunley House
60 Pitcairn Road
Mitcham, Surrey CR4 3LL
Telephone 0181 640 5431

Alzheimer's Disease Society
158–160 Balham High Road
London SW12 9BN
Telephone 0171 306 0606

British Association for Epilepsy
Anstey House, Hanover Square
Leeds
Telephone 0345 089599

Carers' National Association
29 Chilworth Mews
London W2 3RG
Telephone 0171 723 8130

Council and Care
Twyman House, 16 Bonny Street,
London NW1 9PG

Disabled Living Foundation
380–384 Harrow Road
London W9 2HU
Telephone 0171 289 6111

Encephalitis Support Group
Ms Elaine Dowell
Pasture House, Normanby
Sinnington, Yorkshire YO6
Telephone 01751 433318

The Health Education Authority
Hamilton House, Mapledon Place,
London WC1H 9TX

Headway – National Head Injuries Association
7 King Edward Court
King Edward Street
Nottingham NG1 1EW
Telephone 0115 924 0800

Help the Aged
16–18 St James's Walk
London EC1R 0BE
Telephone 0171 253 0253

Mental Health Foundation
37 Mortimer Street
London W1N 7RJ

MIND – National Association for Mental Health
Granta House, 15–19 Broadway
Stratford, London E15 4BQ
Telephone 0181 519 2122

NCVO – National Council for Voluntary Organizations
26 Bedford Square
London WC1B 3HU
Telephone 0171 636 4066

National Society for Epilepsy
Chalfont Centre for Epilepsy
Chalfont St Peter, Buckinghamshire
Telephone 01494 873991

Parkinson's Disease Society
22 Upper Woburn Place
London WC1H 0RA

The Princess Royal Trust for Carers
16 Byward Street, Tower Hill
London EC3R 5BA

**RADAR – Royal Association for
Disability and Rehabilitation**
12 City Forum, 250 City Road
London EC1V 8AF
Telephone 0171 250 3222

The Stroke Association
CHSA House
Whitecross Street
London EC1Y 8JJ
Telephone 0171 490 7999

Women's Royal Voluntary Service
234–244 Stockwell Road
London SW9 9SP

North America

**Alzheimer's International and
Alzheimer's Association of the USA**
The International Federation of
Alzheimer's Disease & Related Disorders
Inc., 919 North Michigan Avenue,
Chicago, Illinois 60611–1676
Telephone 312 335 5777

**Alzheimer's Treatment
& Research Center**
640 Jackson Street, St. Paul, MN 55101

Arizona Bridge to Independent Living
1229 East Washington Street, Phoenix
AZ 85034

Brain Injury Association, Inc.
1776 Massachusetts Avenue, NW
Suite 100, Washington, DC 20036
Telephone (202) 296 6443
Facsimile (202) 296 8850
Internet http://www.biausa.org

Epilepsy Foundation of America
4351 Garden City Drive, Landover
Maryland 20785-2267

Dr Gary Goodman
10211 North Third Street, Suite A4
Phoenix, AZ 85028

International Brain Injury Association
1776 Massachusetts Avenue, NW
Suite 100, Washington, DC 20036
Telephone (202) 835 0580
Facsimile (202) 835 0584

Ontario Head Injury Association
PO Box 2388 'Sth B', St Catherines,
Ontario, Canada L2M 7MF

Europe

Alzheimer's Europe
c/o ECAS, Troonstraat 98–8, B–1050
Brussels, Belgium

Australia

Alzheimer's Association of Australia
PO Box 51, North Ryde, NSW 2113
Telephone 02 878 4466

New Zealand

Adards New Zealand
P O Box 2808, Christchurch
Telephone 03 365 1590

Note

Readers in other countries who want to find out details
of similar organizations in their own area are advised to
contact a local advice centre, carers' group, volunteer
centre or reference library.